To Fred and Ian.
with
fond Aloha

SWEET PARADISE

Helen.

Christmas 1986.

SWEET PARADISE

By Diana Hansen-Young
Book Design by Teresa Gates

Mutual Publishing of Honolulu

This book is for my husband and best friend, Gordon

SWEET PARADISE

First Edition, April 1986
Library of Congress Catalog Card Number 86-060369
ISBN: 0935180-52-4

Produced by Bennett Hymer
Mutual Publishing of Honolulu
2055 N. King Street
Honolulu, Hawaii 96819

All that is Hawaii, is reflected in its women.

From Pele, the fiery goddess of the volcano, to Laka, sensual goddess of the dance, to the great earth mother Hinahina, to the powerful chiefesses and queens, women have bound this land together.

They are the earth, the essence.

They dazzle all with spirit, life, phosphorescence. Their exuberance embraces everyone. Their energy holds their families together. Every day, they reveal hidden treasures: gold, fire, and a core as hard as steel.

They have bound father to son with a caress. They have suffused all with vibrations of play, and dance. Their tears have washed away pain, nourished, healed, and all they have touched has become luminous.

Their strong hands have worked. Their ancient shoulders have borne the children of their womb, and the grief of centuries.

In the night, they have stood vigil over those who sleep, are sick, have need. And at dawn they have reached still deeper for that hidden core of strength, banishing fear and weariness with prayer and hope.

They have given birth. Washed. Dressed. Buried. Renewed, refreshed, replenished. Defied.

They are the common thread, the golden thread that ties us together and binds us to this land.

Sweet Paradise is a hymn to all women, a hymn to the continuous rhythms that beat within the female soul of these islands.

It is a hymn to Hawaii, for indeed, Hawaii is a woman, and all women who love this land are true Hawaiian women.

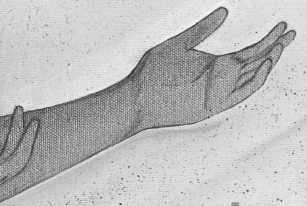

CHAPTER ONE

THE ISLANDS

.... this enchanted place

She chanted a creation mele, and gave birth to Oahu, son of Lua . . .

diana hansen-young '86

NUUANU PALI DRIVE

I saw a woman in white among the vines
on the old Nuuanu Pali Drive.

She shimmered above the ground,
a luminescent vapor,

smiled,
vanished.

Who was she?
Did she know me?

KAILUA BEACH

She looked out the window:
(Snow, slush-grey sidewalks,
faces blanched by cold)
And called up a memory:

Dusty ironwoods, pearlescent sand,
Terns and rainbow sailboats
and the mysterious house
set high into the rocks
of Lanikai Point.

diana hansen-young 86

WAIKIKI

Grandpa courted grandma all summer, and when it was fall, he took her dancing at the Moana. "Let us walk on the pier," he said, and she nodded, blushing, for she knew what he meant.

The new moon coated the water with silver. It illuminated the spooning couples and turned the rough wooden planks into a shining, magic road. In the grand tradition of the old pier, he kissed her and asked for her hand.

When she was eighty-five, she gave me her wedding hat, and pale rose veil. They smelled of ilima.

I wore them last Sunday afternoon to visit Waikiki.

WAIANAE

My mother fished by day for ahi, and by
night tied up her boat at Pokai Bay.

My mother, with seven children, sat on the
dock and drank beer and sang Hawaiian
songs.

My mother, tough as the black rocks of
Makua Cave, never apologized for having
no husband.

When I had my second child, I, too, did not
apologize. "This is the way my mother
raised us," I told my daughter. "And this is
the way we will live."

KO'OLAU-POKO

The sky over Mokolii
is covered with clouds
bearing the lonely rain named ua 'Apuakea.

Malama pono! Be careful!,
women of Ko'olau-poko,
dark eyes, liquid eyes, impertinent eyes,
and rich, fine hair:
jealous Hi'i-aka
may change you, too, to rain.

KOKO KAI

The trees reach down to the rocks, which line the sea. The reef is shallow, full of shining pools. In the water, all is motion, life, light, and phosphorescent color. I stare at my reflection, broken only by my toes in the water. Is my nose too long? I have my father's nose.

ALA WAI

Before all spoken things
was the sea.

We sent our boats
out upon her,
our hana aloha,
to color the dreams
of those we love —
and turn their thoughts to us
while they are sleeping.

I spend an hour
of idle dreaming
at the Ala Wai harbor:
Such is my exile.

Kahiko gave birth to the mist-white waves, and a name song was
chanted for the great island of Maui . . .

UPCOUNTRY MAUI

They rode their horse named Omar Ching all over the fields of Kula. Late in the day, they stopped to rest in the shade of some ironwood trees. "Look, Tati," said Allen, pointing to the distant steeple. "See the church up there? That's the Church of the Holy Ghost." But Tati wouldn't look. All Duane said was "Show-off!", in a crabby voice. They were all tired, and just wanted to go home.

In Hana, we stayed with Auntie Leimomi. On Sunday, she put on our dresses and sent us off to church. "Hurry now," she fussed, braiding my sister's hair too tight. "Don't be late."

We explored a shortcut home from church . . .

. . . and found a little cave in the rocks. Surrounded by mangrove roots and vines, I felt to be in another space and time. My sister was only worried. "Now our dresses are dirty," she said, "and Auntie will surely scold us."

LAHAINA

I want to see the world;
My thirst is too big for Lahaina.

An endless day
by seven sacred pools
And then, dusk.
Who can tell when the light ends,
and the night begins?

It hardly matters.
The little wind named Kā'ili-aloha
blows down from Kipahulu.
The night is cool,
and I welcome the warrior ghosts of Hana
to come to me tonight,
when sleep
rests upon me like a crown.

The great earth mother Hina chanted a mele for her child, Molokai . . .

Summertime
on uncle's ranch
on Molokai:

Orange-red Kikania leis,
the sacred kukui grove,
the political rallies —
    (poached venison, dried aku
    and the piano unloaded
    from the undertaker's van)
and a fawn pet that ate from my hand.

Molokai summer.

diana hansen-young '05

She chanted a song for Kauai: Beautiful Kauai, she sang, you are mine.

THE KISS

I awoke in Hanalei
A hostage of love.

O Kauai, believe in me
Believe in me . . .

. . . O Kauai,
Naʻu Oe,
You are mine.

diana hansen-young '85

A mele for Hawai'i, firstborn of Wakea
and Kane, conceived in fire and stone . . .

HILO RAIN

The rains of spring hang on the branches in my faraway garden like pearls in the twilight.

O, I long for Hilo and ua hānai, the rain that nurtures the earth.

Paniola.
She rides the
hills of Waimea,
the fields of Kamuela.

The ranch is her home,
her horse is her love,
her dog is her friend.
Paniola.

KONA

Kona was wild, barefoot, free.

Her mother had been the very spirit of Kona before she married the missionary's son and went to live in the proper house in Nuuanu. She bound her hair, donned corsets and velvet and had two children. The son was correct and formal. The daughter was Kona.

A clash of ways, of worlds. Of time, and generations. Two women: Mother, daughter. Nuuanu, Kona.

And in the end, with bittersweet tears, her mother relinquished the last little bit of Kona she had kept hidden in her heart to her daughter.

HOKU WELO WELO

High, high on the mountain Mauna Kea, she saw the blazing comet Hoku Welo Welo tear through the fabric of the night, illuminate the heavens, and set the skies aflame with the rosy light of dawn.
Night torch.

She walks alone
over the rocks
the song she sings
given back by the night wind
blowing in from the sea

Tell me,
Milolii fisherwoman
as you walk alone:
Do you have someone
waiting at home?

Laka danced to honor the two islands, Lanai and Niihau, last born of Papa, and chanted two meles of returning, and not returning . . .

LANAI: A SONG OF RETURNING

My sister moved to Honolulu. When our father died, she came back to Lanai City. I hardly knew her on her returning: new clothes, new hair, new ways. The night she left, we cried: nothing would be the same. The plane disappeared over the Norfolk pines, and I told the night: Be kind to my sister! Protect her till she comes home again!

NIIHAU: A SONG OF NOT RETURNING

My mother was born on Niihau, spoke only Hawaiian, and took a boat to Kauai to give birth to her first child. In the hospital she watched television. In Lihue, she enjoyed the electricity, cars, shops.

She never went back. She could not go back. She had embraced the new ways.

To the very day she died, she did not know if she had made the right choice: Did her family on Niihau miss out on the good life of Kauai? Or did she, on Kauai, miss out on the good life of Niihau?

Sometimes I take her Niihau shell lei out to the beach and hold it up to the channel, to the sea, so it might, at least, have a glimpse of home.

A lonely chant for Kahoolawe . . .

Pele cast down the last, small, flaming stones. They sliced, scorching hot and hissing, into the sea, searing all that was around them, turning salt water to steam.

Pele looked, and nodded with satisfaction: Kahoolawe, and the surrounding reefs.

CHAPTER TWO

WOMEN, HATS, LEIS, AND FLOWERS

. . . my pua lei, my cherished blossoms, my children

My greatgrandmother Yuk Kiu's Chinese ginger jar
sits on a koa table in my Hawaiian grandmother's
parlor. When I visit, I take it down and look inside,
and smell Hangchow.

Plumeria
I breathe:
A joy goes out from me!
I take my hat
And write your name
And travel by the sea.

diana hansen-young '85

diana hansen-young '85

I have seen surrender in the eyes of my sisters.
I tell them:
We have held the world forever on ancient shoulders, and they are strong!
Do not give up! Let your strength be the strength of the Waianaes;
never surrender! never surrender!

AN ALBUM OF WOMEN
— my mother's friends (they grad together)

Light the gifu lanterns
Let the dance go on
Till roselight over Lanikai
Proclaims that it is dawn

diana hansen-young

Leialoha from Waimanalo

Her haole friend

Kai: Hawaiian, Chinese, Filipino, Irish —
everything! Poi Dog!

LEI HILI

On the way, I stopped at a small place I know just off the Likelike. There's a tiny patch of palapalai fern, certainly not enough for a halau, but just right to make one lei hili for me.

diana hansen-young '88

NIGHT BLOOMING CEREUS

The cereus bloomed tonight!
I must pick one
To last me till morning
On this night island.

O BLOSSOM OF ILIMA

OHIA LEHUA

Ohia Lehua drinks the mist
from the mountains
and brings the rain.

diana hawaii-young '86

PAPALE

The relationship was forever broken. She dried her tears.
The solution was clear.
She bought a new hat.
It made her feel alive, young. Her body pulsed with the rhythms of life, love.
She threw back her shoulders, and sallied forth to start anew.

diana hansen-young

HIBISCUS HAT

My hat changes with its flowers.
Last week, it was my jade flower hat.
Yesterday, my pikake hat.
Today, it is my hibiscus hat.

KĀHILI

I smell
but cannot see,
under my window,
far below
among the leaves
gingers grow.

THE PANSY HAT

I saw a woman in Kaimuki with a pansy haku lei around her hat! I rushed to ask her: "Have you just come from Waimea?"

"No, Kamuela," she said. "But my friend, who lives in Waimea, made me this hat from the pansies in her yard."

"My mother grows pansies in her yard in Waimea, too," I told the stranger.

She saw the homesickness in my eyes. "Here," she said, and placed her pansy hat upon my head.

AN ALBUM OF HATS

Straw Hat

Lei Papa

Great Grandma's Sunday Hat

Pua Mohala . . . flower in bloom . . .

Lei Kui, pua melia . . . the plumeria lei . . .

Leimaker

THE MAILE LEI

She opened the old box in her closet. The smell of dried maile took her back to the graduation dance when the young man brought her the sweet maile lei.

She remembered his kiss. She could not remember his name.

AN ALBUM OF FLOWERS:

Na pua nani . . . beautiful flowers . . .

Pua Kenikeni

Pua Pikake

Pua Lokelani

diana hansen-young

. . . orchids . . .

...plumerias...

THE ORANGE HIBISCUS

The hibiscus was orange-red, a flame; she held it gently as if it might burn her hand with its color-heat.

THE RED ANTHURIUM

The flower was like the woman: vivid, colorful, vigorous.

Many wanderers were seduced by the flower, the woman and her strength, and never left.

KAM DAY

My grandmother takes me to Honolulu on Kamehameha's birthday to decorate his statue with flowers. She scolds me: "Don't wear those shorts, that T-shirt, they show your disrespect for our king!"

Grandma stands in a row with her civic club sisters, all dressed in black holokus. A large black hat shades her golden face and hides her white hair. From its brim, an orange ostrich feather droops.

I watch the old women pay homage to their king. Far back in the crowd, in my white cotton muumuu, I can tell which one is my grandma because of the orange feather.

GOLDEN FLOWERS

At night I walk into my garden
and sit under my golden shower tree.
I cannot see its vivid yellow colors
in the darkness, but I can feel the heat
of the magic flowers on my skin.

In the moonlight, my garden turns to a
sea of golden foam and shimmering
golden powders. Flowers become
precious jewels, ivory, jade,
on golden stems. The city of Honolulu
vanishes, and I am in an ancient,
secret world: Lemuria, or old Hawaii.

diana hansen-young '86

Does my strength bother you?
Indeed, I walk as though I own
        the block, the city, the world
I come from Papakolea
        and New England,
Waianae and Seoul,
Anahola, Kwangtung,
        Kyoto, Manila,
    Dublin and Lisbon
    I am the world and
    I am Hawaii
    and I am a little sassy.
    Does it bother you?

diana hansen-young '85

CHAPTER THREE

OHANA

. . . the family gathered:
mothers and fathers,
sisters and brothers,
uncles and aunties,
grandmas and grandpas
cousins and tutus,
hānai and hoʻomakua
and all were named differently
but all were ohana.

GRANDMA, GRANDPA

grandma: can you fix the flower?
grandpa: yes, here . . .
grandma: no a little higher
grandpa: okay . . . like this?
grandma: no, no! It's too high!
grandpa: lower, then
grandma: that's too low . . . auwe, you scratch my head with the pin . . .
grandpa: sorry, here . . . like so.
grandma: that's just right. just right. You lucky, you!
grandpa: I know

O, grandma, grandpa!

IN CELEBRATION: KEIKIS   . . . and we are all one.

TWO SISTERS

My sister flies from San Francisco
Bringing fresh crab and sourdough
With her new clothes, and new luggage.

She returns to San Francisco
With guava jelly, dried saimin, pickle mango
All tied up in old brown boxes.

CHAMBERED NAUTILUS

I am sister to the sea.

diana hansen-young 86

HĀNAI

I could have no children, so my sister gave me her daughter, Malia, at birth.
In the hānai tradition of Hawaiian families, I raised her as my own.

"Give your sisters a hug," Auntie always said before we went to bed. "And say your prayers. We never know what will happen before the morning comes."

AUNTIE

On May Day, Auntie, who has no children of her own, gets up early and helps us string the leis. She comes to our school programs, and fixes the flowers in our hair. Afterwards, she takes us home with her and lets us stay up late and eat all the haupia.

diana hansen-young '85

His bare skin was warm to her touch. "You love her more than me," she said, with jealousy. But he replied: "I have never given any other woman anything that belongs to you."

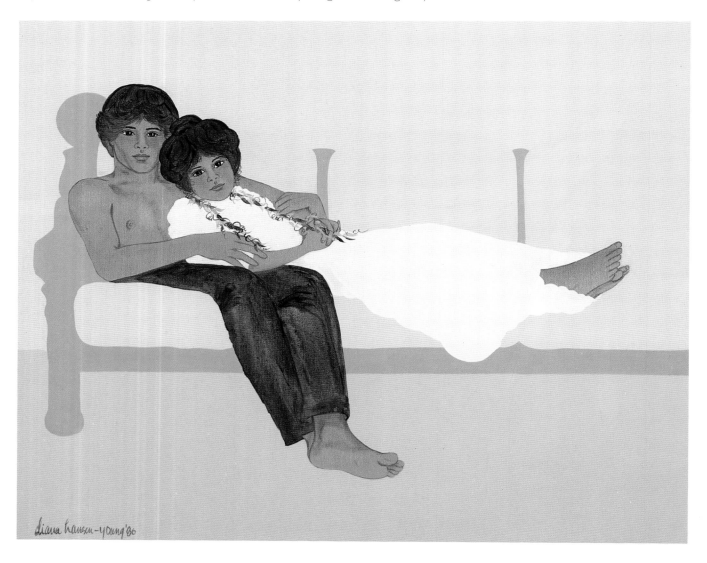

Diana Hansen-Young '86

BROOM POLO

Oh, boy, my sistah! She makes me brush the horse, even wrap his tail in a ripped-up pillowcase we sneaked from home. "It looks more real," she says.

Then she gets to take the first turn of the game. She says she learned to play polo by watching the rich haoles in Honolulu, and that if I watch her, I'll learn how. Except that we have to use brooms for mallets, and my brother's ball.

Not a bad game of broom polo, eh, sistah mine?

KIMO'S WORLD

His great grandma Kinau, who made ninety last week, told him this:
"Women are the essence of this land. If you Hawaiian men are to
grow up without anger, you must have a strong mother, a wife,
who must teach you to love. Before you can truly love,
you must learn to cry. I have always loved a man who can cry.
It means he is not afraid to show his feelings."

diana hansen-young 84

TWO SISTERS

We told each other
all the secret things.
My sister, my love

PI'ILANI'S FAMILY

"We three are family now," she told her two children. "We have each
other, and that is all we need."
But inside, a little fear. Were her words empty? Bravado?
No, she vowed: I will keep my family together. I will care for them,
no matter what the cost. That is my promise.

THREE SISTERS: HINA, LAKA AND HAUMEA

Hawaii today, yesterday and tomorrow

diana hansen-young '84

THREE SISTERS: October 15, 1985.

KONA LULLABY

Pueo hooting,
Makani blowing,
Mele chanting,
Punawai running:

Kona lullaby
for keiki punahele.

diana hansen-young '85

TWO SISTERS

Our life is brief,
Malia my tita.
We are growing older.
We have put away
The secret hiding places
of Kahaluu, and youth

We have moved to the
cities, and have
taken up new lives.

Tonight, as the moths
dance about my windows
wet with evening rain
I cannot forget:
vivid flashes of our youth:
the sea butterflies,
the rhythms of sounds,
the goodbyes of birds.

O, Malia, my tita
My heart is too big:
Everything will change,
and nothing will change.

the secret things.... my sister, my love....   Chana Hansen-Young

WHEN I THINK OF MY CHILDREN . . .

I have sent my children
into the world;
When I think of them
I can do nothing but think of them.

I cannot sleep,
for thinking of my children;
I cannot make mango bread
without thinking of my children.

I cannot go to the beach
Without thinking of my children!

O, my little child,
Who cannot count the passing
Of the days:
Do you know how much I love you?
Do you know how much I love you?

diana hansen-young '86

TUTU'S KOA BED

Tutu invited us to spend the night in great-grandma Kaawaloa Kama's koa bed. My sisters and I decided to fool tutu: We would wait till she fell asleep, and then get up and play. We got into our pajamas and brushed our hair. "Climb in bed," Tutu told us, "and I will tell you a story."

She started to read. I thought I heard a gecko under the bed. "Get back under the quilt," Tutu scolded. "It's not a gecko. Not under Kaawaloa Kama's koa bed! There are no geckos under this koa bed!"

Two sisters equal four bare buns.

diana hansen-yang '86

CHAPTER FOUR

Traditions

O, Malia my tita —
Remember the secrets?

Eh, Malia!
Tonight Chinese New Yeah!

Yeah?
Yeah.

What for do?
Eh, no tell anybody, but,
we go burn firecrackahs tonight!

ALICE MALT SHOP

Auntie Alice had a malt shop in Kaneohe, from way before the war till the late sixties. Us cousins would go down to eat saimin, or help Auntie Alice clean the shop. She is eighty-something now, and worked all her life. "I stay open six in the morning till ten at night, and only fountain service," she says, her white hair immaculately curled under a net. "It was only fountain service."

THE HIKIE'E

Finally, Auntie bought a sofa, but the whole
family still gathers on the hikie'e in the
living room. Maybe it's because it's
a tradition, or maybe it's because
Auntie keeps the sofa covered in plastic!

diana hansen-young '85

PIT BULL COUNTRY

The pit bull who dug his way under her fence into her yard was from Waianae.

The little girl was tougher. She held up her finger. "Sit, you stupid mutt," she yelled.

And he sat.

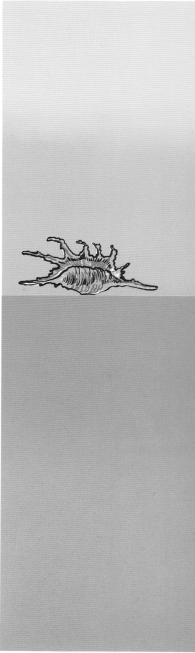

THE SHELL

When I was very small, my uncle went on a mission to Hawaii. He came back tanned and different. For me, he brought a shell. "Put it to your ear, and you can hear the ocean," he said.

I did. Years later I followed that sound to this land, and never left.

SLIPPERS

My brother wore his old rubber slippers. "Oh, pilau," I told him. "Why you like wear your stink slippers to the party?" "They stay outside the door," he said. "Anyway, they look at yours, they think you haole, you, with those fancy-kine slippers."

CHINATOWN

A rhythm of sound, sight, smell:
The pink boxes of manapua, sushi, fish, char siu, soda,
saimin, bao, five spices and tea, the herbalist and golden
thread noodles and opihi from Molokai at $120 a
gallon!
The rhythm of sound, sight, smells
The pink boxes and golden threads of Chinatown.

MAPUANA'S HAIR

Mapuana's hair was a black waterfall, a jet cascade,
an onyx veil that hung to her knees. We begged
to watch her take it down at night, and put it up
in the morning! It all fit neatly into a bun, and no one
knew how much hair was twisted up on top her head.

She married a proper haole from Maryland and
moved to Baltimore. She came to visit last
Christmas, and we cried at the airport to see that
her hair was a short cap of black curls.

MANGO

The sun is hot
Sweet mango tree
Whose leaves today
Give shade to me.

BOAT DAY

My whole family came to the docks the day I left for college on the mainland.
The boat was tied to land with paper streamers and long flower leis.
The whistle sounded, and there was time only for one last embrace.

I shall never forget the band that played, the women who sang, the tears that
streamed down my face as the ship pulled away from the docks, breaking
the paper streamers, the leis, the bonds that bound me to shore, friends, family.

I thought my heart, too, would break.

As the ship passed Diamond Head I threw my leis, one by one, into the
azure sea. I willed them to drift back to shore. I willed that I would return.

I did return, later, much later, after the war. But it was to a land
much changed, scarred, new.

Never again was I to feel the intense, bittersweet sorrow of boat day
in old Honolulu.

CANOE

The wind was sweet and feminine, named Koʻolau-
wahine, and came off the north of Niihau.
It filled the sails of my canoe, and I made shore at
Kauai by nightfall.

diana hansen-young '05

Tutu remembers: "When I was a girl, the best riders were picked to be the pa'u princesses. Pa'u riding started when the girls rode home from church, dressed in their finery, on horseback. They would gallop around Kapiolani Park and look at the young men riding the other way on their horses. The old folks, in their carriages, rode slowly around the outside to keep an eye on everyone. We went fast! We were show off! "Get out of our way, old folks in buggies! There is no room for you!" we said.

Tutu continues: "I guess the young folks do the same thing today, but now they call it cruising."

PICTURE BRIDE

I cannot imagine the feelings of my grandmother as she posed to have her picture taken, to be sent to strange men to look and pick.

My grandfather chose her. She had eleven children and made buttons for Chinese tailors to pay to send them all to Japanese language school.

Did they love each other? Was she happy? Did she ever wish for any other life?

What were the thoughts and feelings of my grandmother as she posed to have her picture taken, to be sent to strange men to pick and choose?

How much time have I spent
on the useless tasks
of daily life

when I could have spent
my time
eating shave ice
at Sandy Beach?

diana hansen-young '86

"YOU ARE CORDIALLY INVITED TO A LUAU
IN HONOR OF
BABY KELII'S FIRST BIRTHDAY"

Auntie Pua pinned ilima in sister's hair.

Sister played the ipu and danced three hulas.

Auntie Melody did a sassy hula.
One man shouted for more,
and uncle punched him in the mouth.

. . . and at midnight,
they ate sweet potatoes and the rest of
the opihi grandma bought in Chinatown.

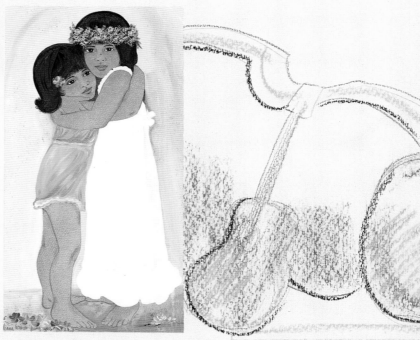

The men finished the beer and rolled up the luau paper. Auntie Melody passed out centerpieces, and Malia's
mother said it was time to go home. Malia wanted to give Kelii a birthday hug, but he was sleeping.
So she hugged Kai instead.

Grandma and her three daughters brought bass,
guitar and ukuleles and made the music . . .

From the painting on
my feather fan
Comes magic, music:
Moonbeams dance
on silk-thread waves,
and pale rose cobwebs
gleam with dewdrops
on the little trees.

A scene from a
remote place:
I dream, (sweet paradise!)
and hold my
feather fan.

diana hansen-young '86

CHAPTER FIVE

THE MAGIC

The sun gold-leafed the sea.
The clear jade waves returned the magic shell they took from me.
The waves are as elusive as a dream. I look at them, and am not sure of anything that has happened.

CHINATOWN

Who? Who is at my window?
Who?
Mystery
Night Island
Chinatown.
Who? Who lives in all those upstairs rooms?
Who?
Deboutonnment
Night Island
Chinatown
What? What are they doing as I pass by their window?
What?
Existence
Night Island
Chinatown

NOH MASK

It was rigid, tight, and made of clay.
I found it in my mother's closet, and put it on to play.

A disguise? Cool, detached, I found her kimono jacket
and slipped it on. It fit,

and I looked in the mirror, and thought to find the most
intimate secrets of my mother:

Hidden treasures, gold, strength, her porcelain beauty,
enamel, silk, that fed her fires within.

There were no secrets. I stared at the face that stared
back at me. I found I was my mother, and she was me.

THE PROMISE

It was almost evening. The mynah birds had started to quarrel on the roof when the old man knocked.

She opened the door at once. He placed his hand on her shoulder and told her softly, so softly she could barely hear his words for the raucous chatter over her head.

Later, much later, she spoke. "What will happen now?" she asked the old man, looking at her sleeping child.

"I don't know," he said gently, and the sadness of the generations and of the sea was in his eyes.

Near dawn, she thought she felt his presence beside her. She awoke, and found nothing. She knew that would be all there ever was.

"I can only find him again in my sleep, and in my dreams," she told herself sadly.

And with the light, the mynah birds did not reply, as they knew that what she said was true.

MIRROR OF TIME

Another time, another place
another face in my mirror.
She wore a hat of straw,
and held a golden fan.
And said, in a voice
made husky with the smoke of a
thousand theaters:
Tell me, Noelani:
Were we young, so long ago?

THE DREAM

The noise of a faint mele ho'ala woke me. Suddenly, all around, was motion and rustling, the sweet scent of mokihana, maile, pakalana. The room was filled with dancers, a ghostly halau, 'ōlapa, ancient ho'opa'a. I heard a calling song, a mele kāhea, my name.

Was it a dream? But in the morning, bits of dried likolehua and crushed uki grass by my bedroom door . . .

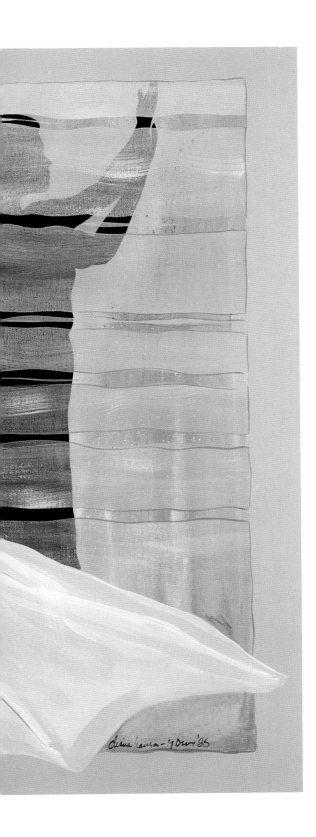

THE DANCE

. . . and I thought: how long has it been since I have danced on the lawn?

All flowers are magic.

I looked into a hibiscus
And suddenly I
saw a band of herons across a rain-drenched sky
I stood,
arms outstretched.
They swooped low,
and carried me away.

In my dream window
Another woman:
My sister,
My self.

diana hansen-young '85

THEY NAME THE RAINS

In this land, they name the rains.
The sweet morning rain is named koʻiawe.
The bitter night rain is called ka uaʻawa.

When the heavens weep, the earth smiles.
I open my umbrella against the bitter rain.

diana hansen-young 86

Dawn will find me
At water's edge
The ghost crabs have gone,
fled,
across the sands,
their tracks
have disappeared.

Dawn will find me
at water's edge
I've fled
Across the waters
my tracks
have disappeared

Those who will follow me
will never know
which way I've gone.

A NOTE FROM THE AUTHOR

I would like to deeply thank all the real people who were the models and inspiration for the paintings and the prose in this book. From the checkout clerk at the supermarket, to the tutu in Waimanalo, to the stranger on the street, to friends, acquaintances, relatives — thank you! You are real and you are beautiful; the true spirit of this land is in your eyes.

A special thanks to Heidi and Thekla, family and friends for their support, patience, and encouragement during the months of painting; to Bennett, for believing in me; to Teresa, for superhuman graphics and to Linda, who has endless courage and endurance.

An acknowledgement of gratitude to the Fujiokas and Light, Inc.; Eddie, Masa and Larry; to the private collections that own the Statehood and other paintings; to Western States Insurance Company, who owns Hoku Welo Welo; to Marjorie Sinclair & her book *Kona* which was the inspiration for the painting of the same name.

A note to Grammar Aficionados: The use of markings to indicate glottal stops, pronunciation, or other diacritical markings, differ from page to page for a reason. Each page was written from a separate point of view, as if extracted from different journals or snatched from bits of conversation of different women. The inconsistency was purposeful, and used to define the particular point of view.

Information regarding posters, prints and paintings for sale may be obtained by writing to The Diana Hansen-Young Company, P.O. Box 428, Kailua, Oahu, Hawaii, U.S.A. 96734.

Information regarding other titles and books in print by Mutual Publishing may be obtained by writing to Mutual Publishing of Honolulu, 2055 N. King Street, Honolulu, Hawaii 96819.

This book was printed and bound by the Hsing Tai Color Printing Company, Taichung, Taiwan.